Playboy's
Classic Cartoons
of the Fifties

Prude

PLAYBOY'S CLASSIC CARTOONS OF THE FIFTIES

WIDEVIEW

BOOKS

To the memory of Jack Cole

Manufactured in the United States of America.

FIRST EDITION

PLAYBOY and Rabbit Head design are trademarks of Playboy, 919 North Michigan Avenue, Chicago, Illinois 60611 (U.S.A.), Reg. U.S. Pat. Off., marca registrada, marque déposée.

Wideview Books/A Division of PEI Books, Inc.

Library of Congress catalog number: 81-50339
ISBN: 0-87223-723-0

"I ain't got no bod-eee . . ."

"Whoopee! Does that bring anything to mind, Miss LaVerne?"

NO, GEORGIE - I CAN'T ASK YOU TO HELP. ITS **MY** PROBLEM -

YOUR PROBLEM? WHY YOU CRAZY, SWEET LITTLE KID!

THERE YOU WERE SITTING IN YOUR RAINCOAT AND BLACK STOCKINGS ON THE LIBRARY STEPS AND YOU SAY ITS **YOUR** PROBLEM -

I ASKED YOU TO HAVE A DRINK - PROBABLY THE FIRST DRINK YOU EVER HAD - AND YOU SAY ITS **YOUR** PROBLEM -

I TOOK YOU DINING EVERY NIGHT FOR A WEEK - THE BEST PLACES! I **KNEW** IT WOULD OVERWHELM YOU - AND YOU SAY ITS **YOUR** PROBLEM

OH, I PLAYED IT SMART ALL RIGHT - I BOUGHT YOU CLOTHES - JEWELRY - AND THEN I PUT YOU UP IN YOUR OWN APARTMENT.

AND WHEN I **KNEW** YOU WERE DAZZLED - DID I TELL YOU IT WAS ALL IMPOSSIBLE? DID I TELL YOU I WAS MARRIED?

NO! I CAME UP LIKE A THIEF IN THE NIGHT AND USED MY DUPLICATE KEY! HOW **ROTTEN** OF ME! HOW **LOW**! AND YOU SAY ITS **YOUR** PROBLEM -

PLEASE GEORGIE - DON'T BLAME YOURSELF -

I'M NOT EVEN SURE IT'S YOURS.

JULES FEIFFER

"Er, that'll be all, folks . . . ahem . . . oh, Mr. and Mrs. Cummings . . ."

"I've been ready for over an hour—you might at least try to be on time for our first date."

'God help you, Hagley, if this ad isn't a success!'

"Sorry, we have no reference books on sex at present. Was there anything in particular you wanted to know?"

"I'm almost sorry I posed for it. It's rather
difficult to live up to now."

"Darling, there's something I should have told you . . .

. . . before we were married.

I'm afraid you're going to be disappointed . . .

. . . and I only hope you won't feel cheated . . .

. . . or hate me for deceiving you.

Darling, my hair is bleached."

"How did a guy like you ever get into a business like this?"

Gahan Wilson

"*I don't know about its buying happiness,*
Mr. Murdock, but money would buy _me_."

"Y-your __wife__? And all the while I thought it was TV!"

"George, someone's been spreading the story you've slept here."

"Tell us more about this California monastery."

"It's morning, Mr. Petroff—time for my screen test!"

"What was that bit about forsaking all others?"

"Now where the hell did he pick up that kind of talk?!"

"Just what kind of a girl do you think I am—a contortionist!"

"I'm sorry, handsome, but I'm afraid you can't charge it to the Diners' Club here."

Gahan Wilson

"Sarah certainly is a friend of the downtrodden."

*"I wonder who this 'secret admirer' is who sends me
a telegram every day at this time."*

"Most men your age would be satisfied
with a little peace of mind."

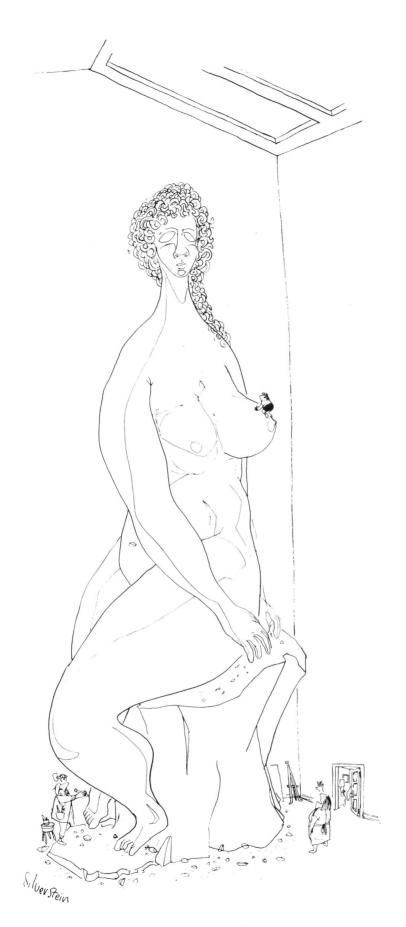

"Irwin . . .!"

"So this is your idea of getting me on canvas . . ."

"You mean all the way from 23rd Street to Central Park?"

"I'll tell you why I hate this island—I'm a leg man."

"And this one we wear in the morning, upon arising."

"'A candid photo of you has just been taken. Handsome prints may be
ordered by addressing . . .'"

*"I'm worried about Sonny. Nineteen years old
and he still plays up in his old treehouse."*

"Here's one ambassador, if they want to recall,
they'll have to come and <u>get</u>!"

"Guess what, Mom. I'm Miss Magic Lift of 1958!"

"How warm do you want me?"

"...Er...have you a king size?"

"But it's not as if we were stealing the song, Charlie. We just borrow the tune and add our own original lyrics. Now in the first line, instead of 'O say can you see,' we put . . ."

"New world or no new world, I'm not getting on __that__ ship!"

"Did you ring, Suzette?"

"Really, Alice Mae, don't you think you're making just a little too much out of this whole thing?"

*"Miss Cummings is out, but if you'd care to come
in anyway, I think I know what to do."*

"The D.A. had my phone tapped . . . now he's up here every night."

FIRST I TRIED INTELLIGENCE.
BUT THEY WOULDN'T PAY ATTENTION.
THEN I TRIED CHARM.
BUT THEY WOULDN'T PAY ATTENTION.
SO I TRIED COMEDY -
AND I TRIED SELF EFFACEMENT-
AND I TRIED MORTIFICATION AND SELF PITY.
BUT THEY JUST WOULDN'T PAY ATTENTION.
SO I GAVE UP AND I QUIETLY WITHDREW.
NOW I'M CONSIDERED INTERESTING.
JULES FEIFFER

"We're running a special this week where you can throw in a green, fuzzy bath towel free."

"Just think, Georgie, someday I'll look just like that!"

"Mr. Van Eppingham wishes me to say that he
gives up and it's your turn to be 'it'!"

*"Welcome home, Eddie-boy—how does it feel
to be out of uniform?"*

*"When you come right down to it, Mr. Bigelow—
casting for TV is just like for movies."*

"*I understand he comes from a very good family.*"

"*I'm on jury duty!!*"

"*I wonder whose wife that was!*"

"Amalgamated Dynamics? I've got you another qualitative electronics engineer."

"You've got a pretty fair line-up here, Abdul, but the trouble is, you lack depth. Now, if I were you I'd trade off one or two of your veterans for some promising young rookies. That way you'll have plenty of reserve strength in case any of your first stringers give out and have to lay off for a while."

*"It lies entirely in our province, Miss Templeton, to establish
an altitude record of sorts right now . . ."*

"Another good story I heard that year
was the one about . . ."

"Hey, Charley, here comes that babe I've
been raving about!"

"How would you like to curl up with a good
bookworm some evening?"

"Virgin Islands? Doesn't sound like a place with any men."

*"Very well, Carter, you've proven my theory faulty—
let it go at that!"*

"*Goodness, Mr. Blandorf—I thought only stars got their own private dressing rooms!*"

"Well, there's history repeating itself."

"Sedgewick, will you please go to sleep?"

"S-a-ay! This looks like a pretty exciting place!"

"Oh, no—not another art class!"

"I hope he isn't counting on any virgin wool from her."

"Good afternoon, sir. I represent the Universal Life Insurance Company . . . uh . . . oh, never mind."

"I guess the young folks decided to go out after all."

"I've been thrilled by the dazzling breakaway of your four-speed, close-ratio, synchromesh manual transmission and the lusty surge of your 315-horsepower, fuel-injection, high-lift cam engine . . ."

"*I assure you that your feeling of not being wanted is all in your mind.*"

"I'm beginning to believe Barnum was right."

"I do hope the natives of this new planet prove friendly."

"We never kiss any more."

Persuadable

Veteran

Nympho

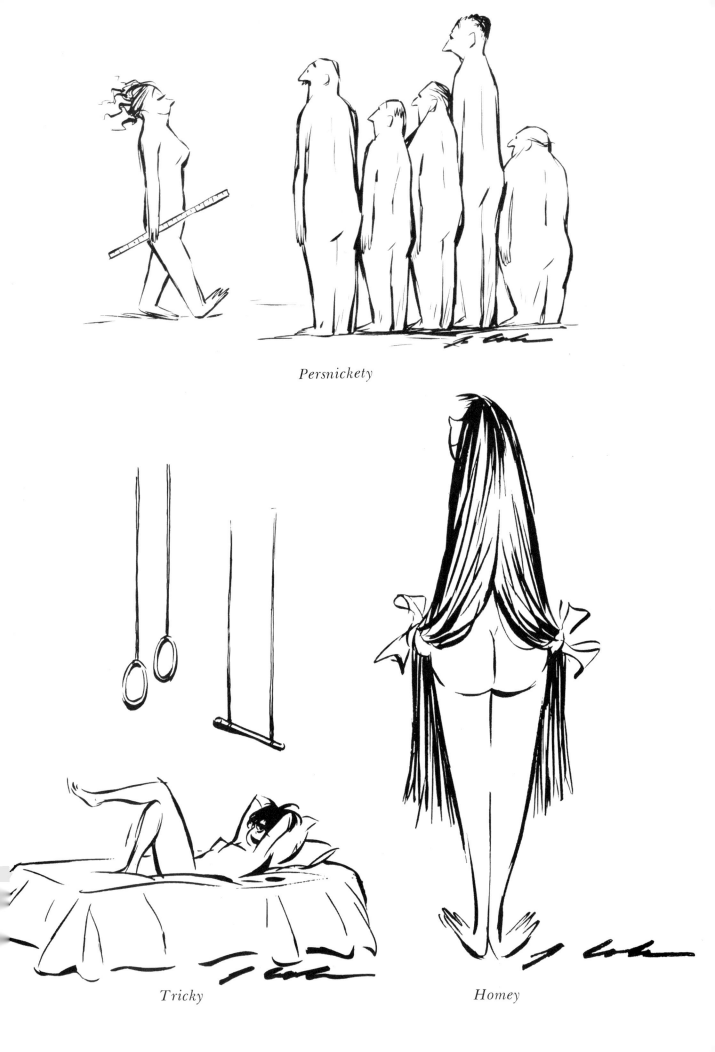

Persnickety

Tricky

Homey

"Where the hell were you when I was down here skindiving?"

"Anything else, boss?"

Gahan Wilson

"It's my husband, but relax—he's sneaking into your apartment across the hall."

"I wanted to start my own bank."

"You're confusing me, Miss Barlow."

*f she tumbles, you said it—otherwise, I said it.
Is that the way it's going to be?"*

*"For heaven's sake, Ed—stop apologizing!
As far as I'm concerned, it never happened!"*

"...These happy, childlike, carefree people. They are,
especially the young girls, so delightfully naive about sex..."

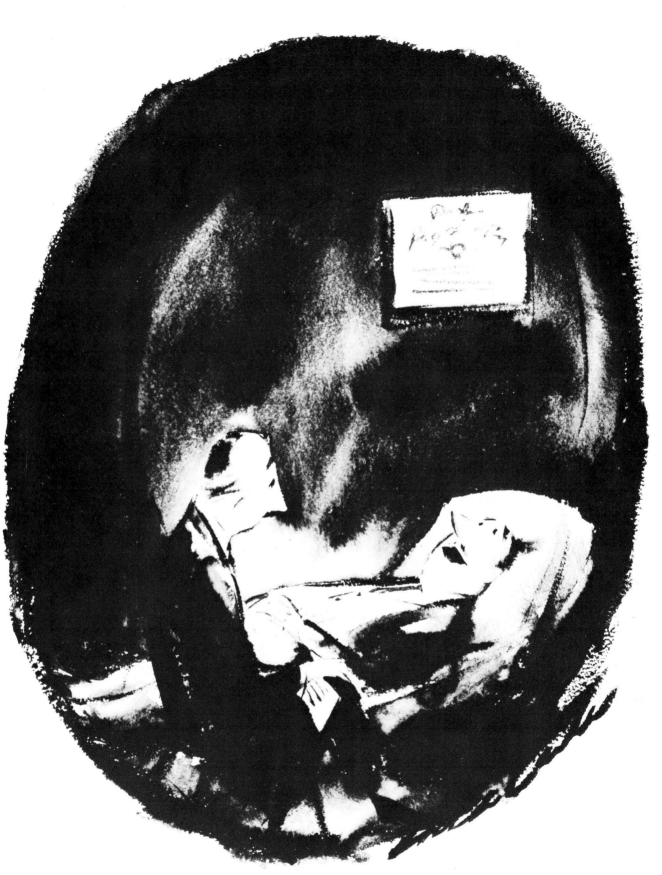

"In the beginning, I created the heaven and the earth ..."

"Goodness, no! It's for the water cooler."

"In case I forget later on in the evening,
the answer is 'No!'"

"Isn't Ted wonderful? Most husbands would have a fit if
their mother-in-law moved in on them."

"Her name is Ellen Rogers, folks . . .
and where do you live, Miss Rogers?"

"Well, that's not what I mean
by playing grown-ups!"

". . . You don't see crime in our fair city under
Mayor Hale . . . you don't see graft under Mayor
Hale . . . you don't see prostitutes under . . ."

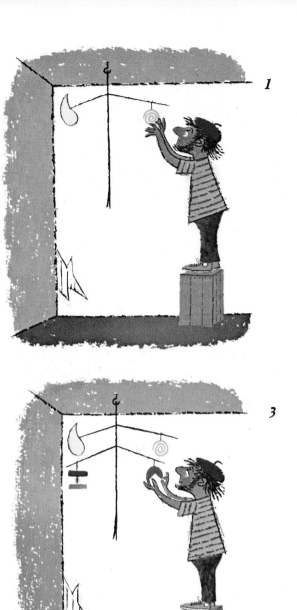

1

3

4

5

6

"Whoa!"

Gahan Wilson

"There's another one of those abominable mountain climbers."

"Care to glance in the mirror?"

"I'm afraid, Miss Kipulski, we are
running out of clay."

"Dammit, what's the matter with you people?
"She's my daughter, I tell you!"

"We can't go on meeting like this, Charles. My husband is getting suspicious."

"Well, good night, gang—it's time I was crawling into the sack."

"I guess we're through—she returned everything I gave her."

"Oh, San Quentin is OK for a short stretch,
but I certainly wouldn't want to do life there!"

"Oh, if you'd only listened to your old
mother! How I begged you . . . reasoned
with you . . . pleaded with you—'Have the
get-away car overhauled!'—But no . . ."

"Sure . . . when he pulled off that Brinks job,
he was your son . . . now he gets nabbed
and he's my son! . . ."

"They won't be here for another 15 minutes—how about one for the road?"

*"Poor Charles hasn't sold a thing in months, but I get
an average of 20 offers a week."*

"Shall we join them?"

"Your first visit to Cannes?"

"What's a matter? Don't I get any orange juice?"

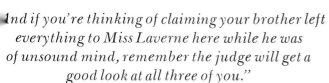

"And if you're thinking of claiming your brother left
everything to Miss Laverne here while he was
of unsound mind, remember the judge will get a
good look at all three of you."

"Then I buried his head in the sports
page. He would have liked that."

"Feelthy peectures stressing togetherness?"

"Hold it! Hold it!"

"Yessir, he was a great park commissioner!"

*"By George, you're right—that nightie has shrunk!
How about shrinking the others?"*

*"Rules are rules, Madam. I suggest you write him a letter
in care of the club."*

"I know the cutest story, but it isn't for
mixed company. Will you ladies leave the room?"

"Having lived a rich and full life . . ."

"Quick, think of some way to get arrested!"

"Of course, it isn't always like this—last trip we carried camel manure."

"I don't care what the Russians claim—it can't be done wearing these damn space suits, floating around a room without gravity!"

*"And just where have you been?...Your horse
came home an hour ago..."*

*"See here, Sir John—what did I tell you about
getting out of bed?!"*

"It's cute, Benson, but will the kiddies go for it?"

"Gee, that's funny—all he gave me was a written exam."

"Well, it's been fun, kid, and if you ever get over to Harrisburg, Pa., be sure to give me a buzz!"

The Seduction by Jules Feiffer

"Congratulations, sir! You're our 10,000th customer!"

"It must be fate—my wife and your husband breaking their legs on the same day!"

"Well, you can, if you want to ..."

Silverstein

"What, never?"

"It's disgusting how they'll commercialize anything!"

"Fake it."

"I offered to donate it to the church bazaar, but Pastor Johnston said he wouldn't think of letting me part with it."

"I told you if we were late we'd miss all the fun."

*"Oh, Harold left an hour ago, Dad—this is
Richard, the milkman."*

"Make it one for my baby and one more for the road."

Gahan Wilson

"Looks like the end of civilization as they know it."

Index of Artists

Conceited